MORE PRAYERS

Illustrated by
TASHA TUDOR

BokBooks International

First published in Great Britain, 1964

This impression 1989

Lutterworth Press
P.O. Box 60
Cambridge CB1 2NT

Co-published in Southern Africa
by Bok Books c.c.,
Manzini, Swaziland
and Durban, R.S.A.

ISBN 0-947444-40-8

Printed in Singapore

To
dear
Cousin Nan

He prayeth best, who loveth best
All things both great and small;
For the dear God who loveth us,
He made and loveth all.
Samuel Taylor Coleridge

Be my guide, O Lord, I pray,
Lest I stumble on my way.
Be my strength, dear Lord, I ask,
That I may fulfill each task.

Be my light, that I may see
What thou does require of me.
Keep me, Lord, both day and night,
Pure and sinless in thy sight.

Elfreyda Wightman

O Lord, open my eyes, to see
what is beautiful:
My mind, to know what is true,

My heart, to love what is good,
For Jesus' sake.

O Jesus, I have promised
To serve thee to the end;
Be thou forever near me,
My Master and my Friend.
I shall not fear the battle
If thou art by my side,
Nor falter in the conflict
If thou will be my guide.

J. E. Bode

Lord, our hearts to thee we raise
In songs of thankfulness and praise.

Bless us, Lord, and grant that we
Good and true and brave may be.

Teach me, my God and King,
In all things thee to see,
That what I do in anything,
To do it as for thee.

George Herbert

All good gifts around us
Are sent from Heaven above,
Then thank the Lord, O thank the Lord,
For all His love.

Jane Montgomery Campbell

Make a joyful noise unto the Lord,
all ye lands.

Serve the Lord with gladness:
come before his presence with singing.
Psalm 100

The earth is the Lord's
and the fulness thereof:

The world,
and they that dwell therein.

Psalm 24

Let all the world in every corner sing
My God and King!
The heavens are not too high,
His praise may thither fly;
The earth is not too low,
His praises there may grow.
Let all the world in every corner sing
My God and King!

George Herbert

I come in the little things,
Saith the Lord:
Not borne on the morning's wings
Of majesty, but I have set My feet
Amidst the delicate and bladed wheat.

I come in the little things,
Saith the Lord:
Yea, on the glancing wing
Of eager birds, the softly pattering feet
Of furred and gentle beasts.

I come in the little things,
Saith the Lord.

Evelyn Underhill

Shew me thy ways, O Lord;
teach me thy paths.
Lead me in thy truth, and teach me:

For thou art the God of my salvation;
On thee do I wait all the day.

Psalm 25

When the winter winds are cold,
And the sheep are in their fold;
For my cosy home, and love,
Thank you, Father God, above.

The Lord is my light and my salvation;
whom shall I fear?

The Lord is the strength of my life;
of whom shall I be afraid?

Psalm 27

God, that madest earth and heaven,
Darkness and light;
Who the day for toil has given
For rest the night;

May thine Angel-guards defend us,
  Slumber sweet thy mercy send us,
Holy dreams and hopes attend us,
  This livelong night.

Bishop Heber

Good night, dear Lord, and now
   Let them that loved to keep
Thy little bed in Bethlehem
   Be near me while I sleep:
For I—more helpless, Lord,—of them
   Have greater need than thou.

John Bannister Tabb

Let all those that seek thee
rejoice and be glad in thee:

Let such as love thy salvation
say continually, The Lord be magnified.
Psalm 40

O holy Child of Bethlehem,
Descend to us, we pray;
Cast out our sin, and enter in,
Be born in us today.
We hear the Christmas angels
The great glad tidings tell:
O come to us, abide with us,
Our Lord Emmanuel.

Phillips Brooks